For my brilliant nieces
# Carter, Charlotte & Maria

Special thanks to
Nia Brown

My
Apple
Orchard

# Plant, Water & Nourish

---

Together, let us **plant** seeds of compassion combating division. Let us **water** the deep roots of love that hide under the soil of doubt and fear, let us **nourish** the common good for the shared benefit of all.

I am grateful to the **Common Good Coalition** for being a place where I am free to express my thoughts and the opportunity to bear fair witness to all I have seen, heard & learned along my journey.

Genesis Be

ISBN:  978-0-9997601-8-5 - *hardcover*    ISBN:  978-0-9997601-7-8  - *softcover*

**Genesis Be**

GenesisBe@gmail.com | @GenesisBe

**Illustration & Design**

Tais Lemos | tlemos.com | @taisllemos

**Strive Till I Rise**

strivetillirise.org

**Common Good Coalition**

cgcoalition.com

*Published by **Strive Till I Rise** & **Common Good Coalition***

# My Apple Orchard

Genesis Be

As I walked alone on Emerald Mound
I rested upon a rock

My mind was comforted as I watched the sky
Suddenly, rain did drop

I looked around for shelter
Though I knew that there was none

The closest thing was an apple orchard
It was there that I did run

I rested my body against a trunk
And gazed up in the air

The leaves were thick upon the
Branches

But fruit it did not bear

But on the ground in front of me
An apple I did see

It was fully rotted except the stem
And about three of its seeds

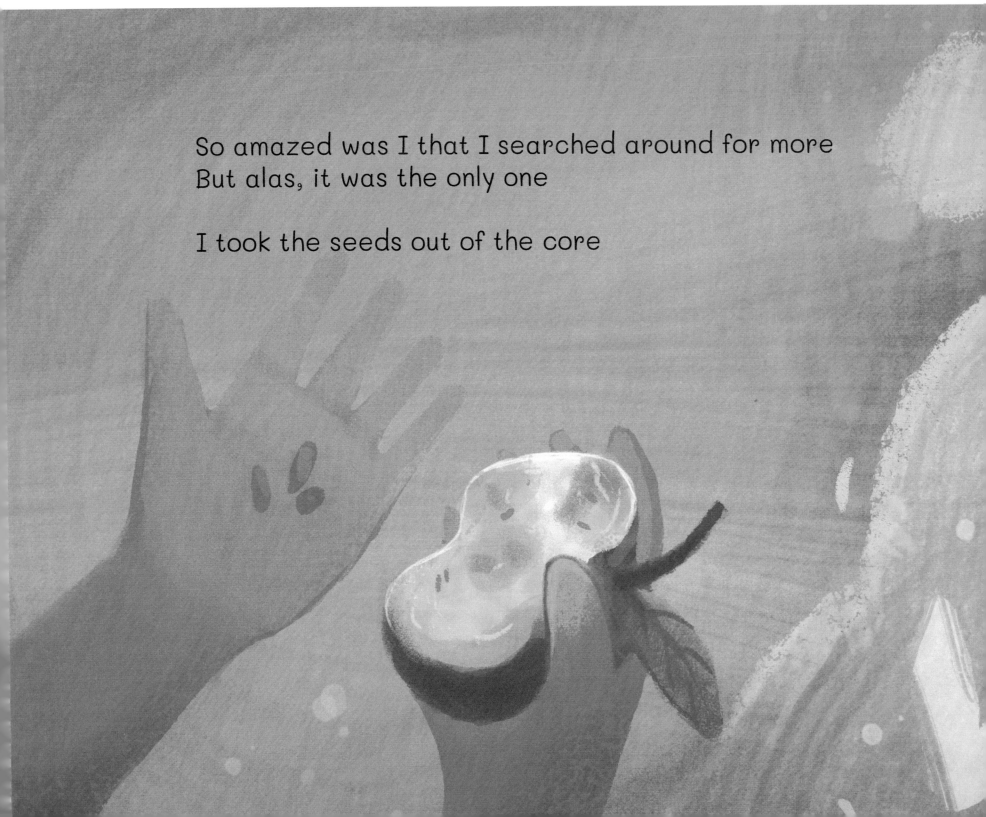

So amazed was I that I searched around for more
But alas, it was the only one

I took the seeds out of the core

The rain did not subside
But I ventured into the storm

The Earth became a darkness
As the thunderclouds did form

I ventured to a place I knew
Was desolate and nothing grew

My left hand held the seeds I keep
My right hand dug a hole so deep

But before I placed them in the Earth
I asked myself "What is the worth?"

If tomorrow the World would cease to exist
Then what is the purpose of doing all this?

But I cast my doubts aside
And the three seeds I did plant

I returned to the city knowing that
One day I would be back

For years I lived abroad traveling to different lands

I saw the triumphs of family and friends

From the shores of Asian isles

To the length of Africa's Nile

From the hills of Scottish countrysides

To the remote lands where no one resides

When my body grew weary
I returned to Mississippi
I first went to the country
Before returning to the city

And when I did arrive
Much to my surprise
From a rotten apple
A beautiful orchard did rise!

So I sat amidst my orchard
Peaceful and reserved
Eating the ripened apples
Sharing what I had learned

Writing songs & writing poems
As she gazed over my shoulder
She provided shade on sunny days
Together we grew older

I apologized for doubting her so many years ago
For even if the World declines
I'd wish my seeds to grow

The Beginning

My
Apple
Orchard

As a community of seekers, leaders, artists, poets we are always in search of ways to live our lives for the common good. We understand that what is good for others is ultimately good for us as well.

We invite you to join us in this journey ... a path toward discovering how we measure the values and focus of our lives, our work, our play and our faith by the **common good**.

We are pleased to showcase the work of Genesis Be.

**cgcoalition.com**

My
# Apple
Orchard